Andrew Brodie Basics

LET'S DO
TIMES
TABLES

FOR AGES 9-10

with over **100** reward stickers

- Over 300 practice questions
- Regular progress tests
- Thorough tables practice

Published 2015 by Bloomsbury Publishing Plc
50 Bedford Square, London, WC1B 3DP

www.bloomsbury.com

Bloomsbury is a registered trademark of Bloomsbury Publishing Plc

ISBN 978-1-4729-1666-2

Copyright © 2015 Bloomsbury Publishing
Text copyright © 2015 Andrew Brodie
Cover and inside illustrations of Ollie the Owl and Andrew Brodie © 2015 Nikalas Catlow
Other inside illustrations © 2015 Judy Brown (Beehive Illustrations)

A CIP catalogue for this book is available from the British Library.

1 0 9 8 7 6 5 4 3 2

Printed in China by Leo Paper Products

This book is produced using paper that is made from wood grown in managed, sustainable forests. It is natural, renewable and recyclable. The logging and manufacturing processes conform to the environmental regulations of the country of origin.

To see our full range of titles visit www.bloomsbury.com

BLOOMSBURY

Notes for parents

What's in this book

This is the fifth in an exciting new series of *Andrew Brodie Basics: Let's Do Times Tables*. Each book contains more than 300 multiplication table questions, especially devised to cover the key requirements of the National Curriculum.

At the upper part of Key Stage Two, children are expected to have a thorough knowledge of the multiplication tables so that they can 'multiply and divide numbers mentally drawing upon known facts'. This book features a wide range of practice activities for the two, three, four, five, six, seven, eight, nine, ten, eleven and twelve times tables. Learning the multiplication facts in context will help your child with later work on long multiplication and division. For example, discussing scores on dice will help your child with the early stages of probability while at the same time providing the opportunity to use tables in a potentially real situation. What would be the total if I rolled 4 on each of 6 dice?

How you can help

To get the most out of this book, find time to sit with your child while they work through the activities and discuss the questions with them, explaining any terms they are not familiar with. To begin with, your child may find the activities and progress tests quite tricky and they might get quite a few questions wrong. Make sure that they don't feel disheartened by this. Instead, give your child lots of praise and explain that everyone makes mistakes and that's how we all learn!

The level of difficulty increases gradually throughout the book but some questions are deliberately repeated. This is to ensure that children have the opportunity to revisit vital new facts – they may not know the answer to a particular question the first time they encounter it but with another opportunity later on children are given a second chance. Don't be surprised if they need to practise certain questions lots of times!

You might find it helpful to put up posters on the bedroom wall, showing multiplication facts for all the times tables. Talk about these facts with your child.

Ollie the Owl

Look out for Ollie the Owl who is full of wise comments to help your child through the learning process!

Brodie's Brain Boosters

Brodie's Brain Boosters feature short mathematical problems, which can be solved by working logically. Some of these may look very straightforward but the thinking processes that your child will need to apply are important skills to practise, ready for more challenging work later on. Understanding the wording of questions is a crucial aspect of problem solving so ensure that your child reads each question carefully – give some help with the vocabulary if necessary.

With lots of practice your child will see their marks improve day by day. By the end of the book you should be able to see a real improvement in their maths and hopefully a positive attitude too!

You should be familiar with the two times table!

How quickly can you complete the two times table in words and numbers? Time yourself!

One two is two		1 x 2 = 2
Two twos are		2 x 2 =
Three twos are		
Four twos are		
Five twos are		
Six twos are		
Seven twos are		
Eight twos are		
Nine twos are		
Ten twos are		
Eleven twos are		
Twelve twos are		

Time taken
Seconds

Try the two times table in numbers again. Can you beat your last score? Now use the facts from the two times table to answer the division questions below.

6 ÷ 2 =
24 ÷ 2 =
14 ÷ 2 =
12 ÷ 2 =
2 ÷ 2 =
10 ÷ 2 =
22 ÷ 2 =
16 ÷ 2 =
8 ÷ 2 =
20 ÷ 2 =
18 ÷ 2 =
4 ÷ 2 =

Time taken
Seconds

Brodie's Brain Booster

How many 2p coins are worth the same as a 50p coin?

3

Revising the three times table

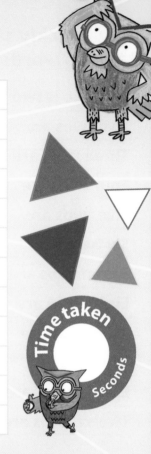

How quickly can you complete the three times table in words and numbers? Time yourself!

One three is three	→	1 x 3 =
Two threes are	→	
Three threes are	→	
Four threes are	→	
Five threes are	→	
Six threes are	→	
Seven threes are	→	
Eight threes are	→	
Nine threes are	→	
Ten threes are	→	
Eleven threes are	→	
Twelve threes are	→	

Time taken ___ Seconds

Try the three times table in numbers again. Can you beat your last score? Now use the facts from the three times table to answer the division questions below.

$9 \div 3 =$
$18 \div 3 =$
$30 \div 3 =$
$27 \div 3 =$
$6 \div 3 =$
$24 \div 3 =$
$21 \div 3 =$
$36 \div 3 =$
$33 \div 3 =$
$15 \div 3 =$
$12 \div 3 =$
$3 \div 3 =$

Time taken ___ Seconds

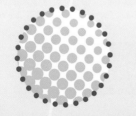

Brodie's Brain Booster

How many sides would 15 triangles have altogether?

4

Multiple stamps!

This page could be tricky!

Each stamp contains a multiple of two or three or both. Write the multiplication or multiplications for that multiple. One is done for you.

18   9 × 2
         6 × 3

9

14

21

15

24

4

12

27

36

16

2

6

30

8

33

10

20

5

Revising the four times table

The answers to the four times table are double the answers to the two times table.

How quickly can you complete the four times table in words and numbers? Time yourself!

One four is four	➡	1 x 4 =
Two fours are	➡	
Three fours are	➡	
Four fours are	➡	
Five fours are	➡	
Six fours are	➡	
Seven fours are	➡	
Eight fours are	➡	
Nine fours are	➡	
Ten fours are	➡	
Eleven fours are	➡	
Twelve fours are	➡	

Time taken

Seconds

Try the four times table in numbers again. Can you beat your last score? Now use the facts from the four times table to answer the division questions below.

8 ÷ 4 =
48 ÷ 4 =
20 ÷ 4 =
32 ÷ 4 =
28 ÷ 4 =
24 ÷ 4 =
40 ÷ 4 =
16 ÷ 4 =
44 ÷ 4 =
36 ÷ 4 =
12 ÷ 4 =
4 ÷ 4 =

Time taken

Seconds

Brodie's Brain Booster
How many sides would 15 squares have altogether?

6

Tables speed

Answer the questions as quickly as you can.

Use the tables you have learnt to help you answer these multiplication and division questions.

7 x 4 =	24 ÷ 2 =	12 x 3 =	9 x 4 =
27 ÷ 3 =	2 x 2 =	4 x 4 =	15 ÷ 3 =
12 x 2 =	11 x 4 =	21 ÷ 3 =	6 x 2 =
16 ÷ 4 =	3 x 3 =	9 x 2 =	36 ÷ 4 =
7 x 2 =	24 ÷ 3 =	48 ÷ 4 =	4 x 2 =
18 ÷ 3 =	5 x 4 =	11 x 2 =	6 ÷ 3 =
28 ÷ 4 =	8 x 2 =	12 ÷ 3 =	12 ÷ 4 =
6 x 3 =	8 ÷ 2 =	36 ÷ 3 =	8 x 3 =

Now try these problems.

Go-karts have four wheels. How many wheels are needed to make 15 go-karts?

Trikes have three wheels. How many wheels are needed to make 20 trikes?

Bikes have two wheels. If a bike factory has 50 wheels in stock, how many bikes can be made?

1 Write the even numbers from 2 to 24.

2 Write the multiples of 3 from 3 to 36.

3 Write the multiples of 4 from 4 to 48.

4 What would the next multiple of 4 be?

5 Each stamp shows a multiple. Write the multiplication facts for the multiples. Watch out! Some stamps need more than one fact.

21

32

12

18

27

Now answer these questions.

6 $16 \div 4 =$

7 $24 \div 3 =$

8 $22 \div 2 =$

9 $30 \div 3 =$

10 $28 \div 4 =$

11 $36 \div 4 =$

12 $18 \div 3 =$

13 $21 \div 3 =$

14 $18 \div 2 =$

Revising the five times table

The fives always have a zero or a five at the end.

How quickly can you complete the five times table in words and numbers? Time yourself!

One five is five	➡	1 x 5 =
Two fives are	➡	
Three fives are	➡	
Four fives are	➡	
Five fives are	➡	
Six fives are	➡	
Seven fives are	➡	
Eight fives are	➡	
Nine fives are	➡	
Ten fives are	➡	
Eleven fives are	➡	
Twelve fives are	➡	

Time taken ____ Seconds

Try the five times table in numbers again. Can you beat your last score? Now use the facts from the five times table to answer the division questions below.

$35 \div 5 =$
$20 \div 5 =$
$55 \div 5 =$
$5 \div 5 =$
$45 \div 5 =$
$10 \div 5 =$
$40 \div 5 =$
$25 \div 5 =$
$50 \div 5 =$
$60 \div 5 =$
$15 \div 5 =$
$30 \div 5 =$

Time taken ____ Seconds

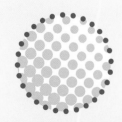

Brodie's Brain Booster

How many 5p coins are worth the same as £1?

The sixes can be tricky to remember.

How quickly can you complete the six times table in words and numbers? Time yourself!

One six is six	→	1 x 6 =
Two sixes are	→	
Three sixes are	→	
Four sixes are	→	
Five sixes are	→	
Six sixes are	→	
Seven sixes are	→	
Eight sixes are	→	
Nine sixes are	→	
Ten sixes are	→	
Eleven sixes are	→	
Twelve sixes are	→	

Try the six times table in numbers again. Can you beat your last score? Now use the facts from the six times table to answer the division questions below.

48 ÷ 6 =
12 ÷ 6 =
30 ÷ 6 =
42 ÷ 6 =
66 ÷ 6 =
72 ÷ 6 =
36 ÷ 6 =
24 ÷ 6 =
6 ÷ 6 =
18 ÷ 6 =
60 ÷ 6 =
54 ÷ 6 =

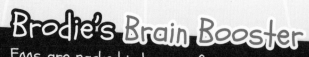

Brodie's Brain Booster
Eggs are packed in boxes of six. How many eggs would there be in 15 full boxes?

More sixes

A hexagon has six sides and six vertices.

Each hexagon contains a multiple of six. Write the multiplication for that multiple. One has been done for you.

48 8 × 6

18

30

42

66

6

24

60

72

36

12

54

Brodie's Brain Booster

How many boxes would be needed for 96 eggs?

Fives and sixes

How quick can you be?

How quickly can you connect each question to the correct answer? Time yourself! Watch out! Two answers will need more than one line.

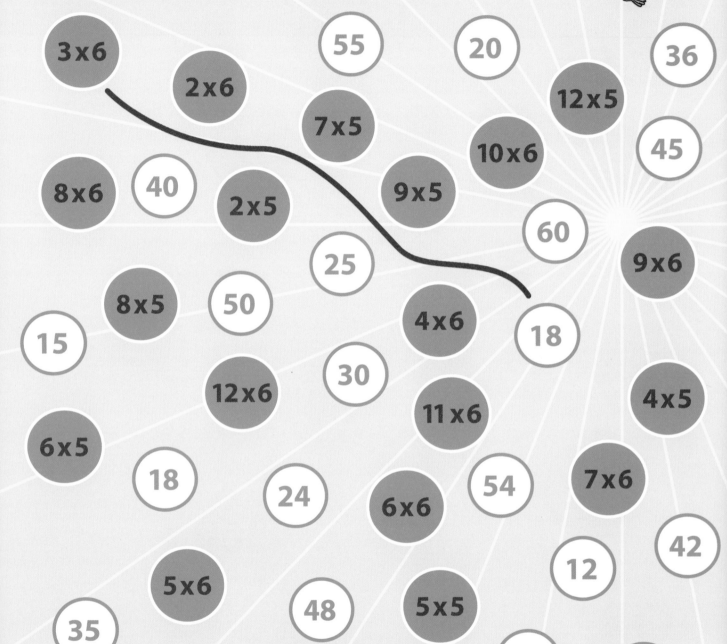

3 x 6

55

20

36

2 x 6

12 x 5

7 x 5

10 x 6

45

8 x 6

40

9 x 5

2 x 5

60

9 x 6

25

8 x 5

50

4 x 6

18

15

30

12 x 6

4 x 5

11 x 6

6 x 5

18

7 x 6

24

54

6 x 6

42

12

5 x 6

48

5 x 5

35

10

66

72

Brodie's Brain Booster

30 and 60 are multiples of both 5 and 6. What is the next multiple of both 5 and 6?

Multiple pictures!

Use your fives and sixes.

Each frame contains a multiple of five or six or both. Write the multiplication or multiplications for that multiple. One has been done for you.

30 6 × 5
      5 × 6

24

42

66

25

72

15

60

45

12

36

10

35

18

20

48

40

54

1 Write the multiples of 6 from 6 to 72.

2 Write the multiples of 5 from 5 to 100.

3 How many eggs would 18 eggboxes hold altogether?

4 How many 5p coins would be needed to make 70p?

5 How much would forty 5p coins be worth altogether?

Now answer these questions.

6 36 ÷ 6 =

7 45 ÷ 5 =

8 24 ÷ 6 =

9 30 ÷ 5 =

10 72 ÷ 6 =

11 55 ÷ 5 =

12 42 ÷ 6 =

13 35 ÷ 5 =

14 48 ÷ 6 =

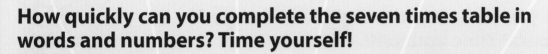

There are seven days in a week

How quickly can you complete the seven times table in words and numbers? Time yourself!

One seven is seven	➡	1 x 7 =
Two sevens are	➡	
Three sevens are	➡	
Four sevens are	➡	
Five sevens are	➡	
Six sevens are	➡	
Seven sevens are	➡	
Eight sevens are	➡	
Nine sevens are	➡	
Ten sevens are	➡	
Eleven sevens are	➡	
Twelve sevens are	➡	

Time taken _____ Seconds

Try the seven times table in numbers again. Can you beat your last score? Now use the facts from the seven times table to answer the division questions below.

42 ÷ 7 =
14 ÷ 7 =
49 ÷ 7 =
84 ÷ 7 =
77 ÷ 7 =
35 ÷ 7 =
7 ÷ 7 =
63 ÷ 7 =
56 ÷ 7 =
28 ÷ 7 =
70 ÷ 7 =
21 ÷ 7 =

Time taken _____ Seconds

Sun	Mon	Tues	Wed	Thurs	Fri	Sat

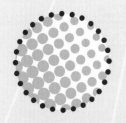

Brodie's Brain Booster

How many days are there altogether in fourteen weeks?

Spiders have 8 legs. Buying shoes must be expensive!

How quickly can you complete the eight times table in words and numbers? Time yourself!

One eight is eight	➡	1 x 8 =
Two eights are	➡	
Three eights are	➡	
Four eights are	➡	
Five eights are	➡	
Six eights are	➡	
Seven eights are	➡	
Eight eights are	➡	
Nine eights are	➡	
Ten eights are	➡	
Eleven eights are	➡	
Twelve eights are	➡	

Time taken — Seconds

Try the eight times table in numbers again. Can you beat your last score? Now use the facts from the eight times table to answer the division questions below.

32 ÷ 8 =
64 ÷ 8 =
80 ÷ 8 =
16 ÷ 8 =
72 ÷ 8 =
56 ÷ 8 =
48 ÷ 8 =
8 ÷ 8 =
40 ÷ 8 =
88 ÷ 8 =
24 ÷ 8 =
96 ÷ 8 =

Time taken — Seconds

Brodie's Brain Booster

How many legs would 15 spiders have altogether?

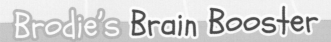

More sevens

A heptagon has seven sides and seven vertices.

Each heptagon contains a multiple of seven. Write the multiplication for that multiple. One has been done for you.

49 7 x 7

21

42

84

56

63

77

7

14

28

70

35

Brodie's Brain Booster

A 50p coin has seven sides. How many sides would fourteen 50p coins have altogether?

17

More eights

Each octagon contains a multiple of eight.
Write the multiplication for that multiple.
One has been done for you.

56   7 x 8   96   16

64   32   48

8   72   88

24   40   80

Brodie's Brain Booster

An octopus has 8 arms. How many arms
would seventeen octopuses have altogether?

18

Multiple circles!

Use your sevens and eights.

Each circle contains a multiple of seven or eight or both. Write the multiplication or multiplications for that multiple. One has been done for you.

48   6 x 8

24

42

64

56

70

16

72

96

28

49

40

80

32

14

35

21

88

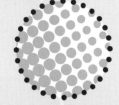

1 Write the multiples of 7 from 7 to 84.

2 What is the next multiple of 7 after 84?

3 Write the multiples of 8 from 8 to 96.

4 What is the next multiple of 8 after 96?

5 Each frame has a multiple shown. Write the multiplication facts for the multiples. One frame has more than one fact.

32

42

56

84

96

Now answer these questions.

6 42 ÷ 7 =

7 48 ÷ 8 =

8 28 ÷ 7 =

9 72 ÷ 8 =

10 56 ÷ 7 =

11 64 ÷ 8 =

12 96 ÷ 8 =

The digits in every multiple of nine add up to 9. Try it!

How quickly can you complete the two times table in words and numbers? Time yourself!

One nine is nine	→	1 x 9 =
Two nines are	→	
Three nines are	→	
Four nines are	→	
Five nines are	→	
Six nines are	→	
Seven nines are	→	
Eight nines are	→	
Nine nines are	→	
Ten nines are	→	
Eleven nines are	→	
Twelve nines are	→	

Time taken Seconds

Try writing out the nine times table in numbers again. Time yourself: can you beat your last score? Now use the facts from the nine times table to answer the division questions below.

36 ÷ 9 =
99 ÷ 9 =
81 ÷ 9 =
108 ÷ 9 =
72 ÷ 9 =
63 ÷ 9 =
45 ÷ 9 =
27 ÷ 9 =
90 ÷ 9 =
18 ÷ 9 =
9 ÷ 9 =
54 ÷ 9 =

Time taken Seconds

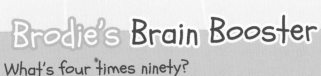

Brodie's Brain Booster

What's four times ninety?

How quickly can you complete the ten times table in words and numbers? Time yourself!

One ten is ten	→	1 x 10 =
Two tens are	→	
Three tens are	→	
Four tens are	→	
Five tens are	→	
Six tens are	→	
Seven tens are	→	
Eight tens are	→	
Nine tens are	→	
Ten tens are	→	
Eleven tens are	→	
Twelve tens are	→	

Time taken

Seconds

Try the ten times table in numbers again. Can you beat your last score? Now use the facts from the ten times table to answer the division questions below.

100 ÷ 10 =
90 ÷ 10 =
40 ÷ 10 =
10 ÷ 10 =
60 ÷ 10 =
70 ÷ 10 =
110 ÷ 10 =
50 ÷ 10 =
30 ÷ 10 =
120 ÷ 10 =
20 ÷ 10 =
80 ÷ 10 =

Time taken

Seconds

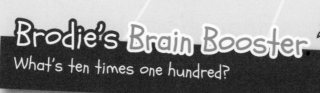

Brodie's Brain Booster

What's ten times one hundred?

More nines

Each nonagon contains a multiple of nine.
Write the multiplication for that multiple.
One has been done for you.

63 7 x 9

99

27

54

18

36

108

72

9

81

45

90

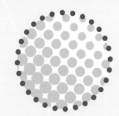

Brodie's Brain Booster

How many sides would 16 nonagons have altogether?

23

More tens

It is easy to multiply any number by 10.

When any whole number is multiplied by 10, the digits move one place to the left and a zero is put in the units column. Look at these examples:

36 x 10 = 360

19 x 10 = 190

642 x 10 = 6420

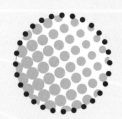

Now try these questions.

43 x 10 =	179 x 10 =	18 x 10 =
864 x 10 =	99 x 10 =	277 x 10=

When a decimal number is multiplied by 10, the digits move one place to the left. Look carefully at these examples:

6.7 x 10 = 67	19.4 x 10 = 194	3.78 x 10 = 37.8
0.5 x 10 = 5	0.25 x 10 = 2.5	23.75 x 10 = 237.5

Now try these questions.

4.5 x 10 =	27.6 x 10 =	4.99 x 10 =
0.7 x 10 =	0.37 x 10 =	48.64 x 10 =

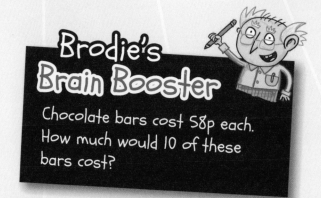

Brodie's Brain Booster

Chocolate bars cost 58p each. How much would 10 of these bars cost?

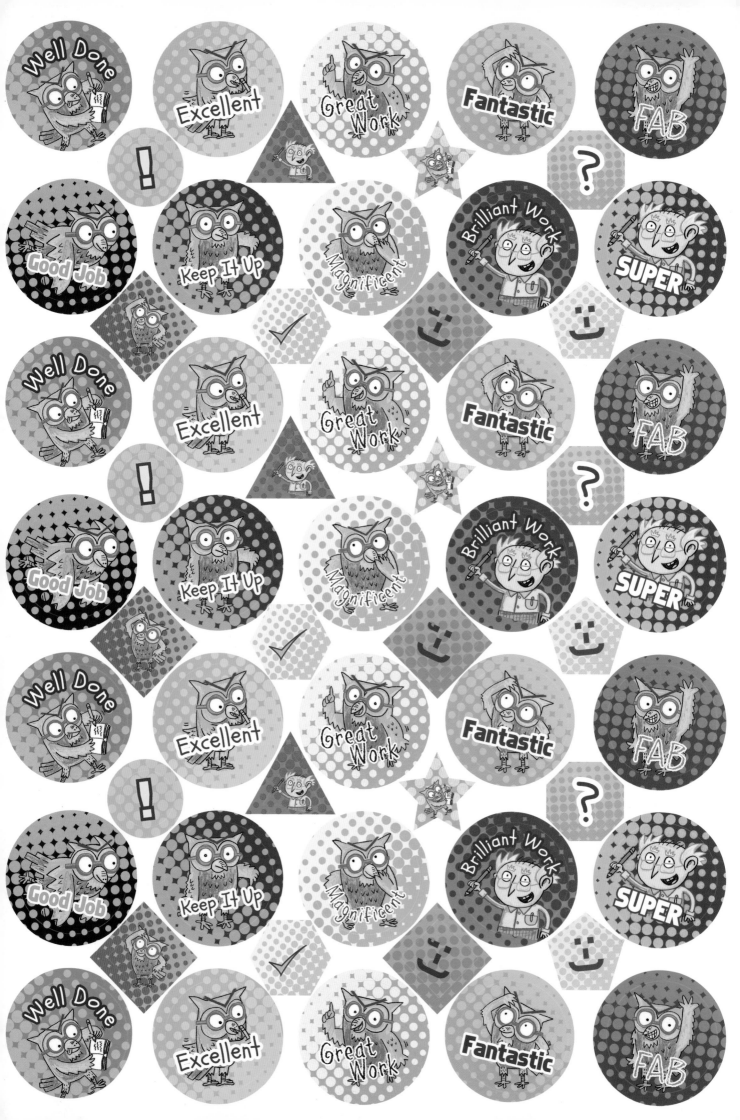

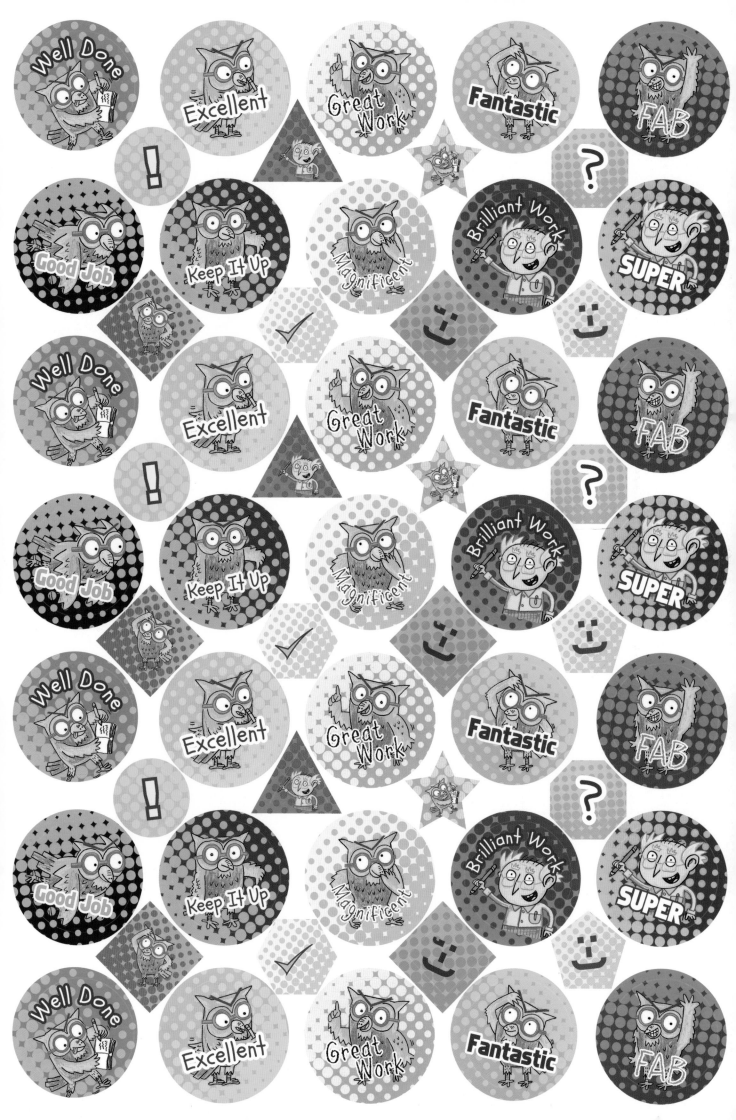

Multiple circles!

Use your nines and tens.

Each circle contains a multiple of nine or ten or both. Write the multiplication or multiplications for that multiple. One has been done for you.

90 10×9
9×10

81

40

27

108

120

72

60

36

80

18

110

63

45

70

99

30

54

25

1 Write the multiples of 10 from 10 to 200.

2 Write the multiples of 9 from 9 to 108.

3 What is the next multiple of 9 after 108?

4 How many corners would 12 decagons have altogether.

5 How many corners would 12 nonagons have altogether?

6 Write the nine times table as quickly as you can.

$1 \times 9 =$			

Now answer these questions.

7 $54 \div 9 =$ **8** $36 \div 9 =$ **9** $81 \div 9 =$

10 $108 \div 9 =$ **11** $12.4 \times 10 =$ **12** $6.35 \times 10 =$

How quickly can you complete the eleven times table in words and numbers? Time yourself!

One eleven is eleven	➡	1 x 11 =
Two elevens are	➡	
Three elevens are	➡	
Four elevens are	➡	
Five elevens are	➡	
Six elevens are	➡	
Seven elevens are	➡	
Eight elevens are	➡	
Nine elevens are	➡	
Ten elevens are	➡	
Eleven elevens are	➡	
Twelve elevens are	➡	

Time taken — Seconds

Try writing out the eleven times table in numbers again. Time yourself: can you beat your last score? Now use the facts from the eleven times table to answer the division questions below.

121 ÷ 11 =
33 ÷ 11 =
66 ÷ 11 =
11 ÷ 11 =
110 ÷ 11 =
99 ÷ 11 =
55 ÷ 11 =
22 ÷ 11 =
88 ÷ 11 =
132 ÷ 11 =
77 ÷ 11 =
44 ÷ 11 =

Time taken — Seconds

Brodie's Brain Booster

What's 15 times 11?

There are twelve months in one year.

How quickly can you complete the twelve times table in words and numbers? Time yourself!

One twelve is twelve	→	1 x 12 =
Two twelves are	→	
Three twelves are	→	
Four twelves are	→	
Five twelves are	→	
Six twelves are	→	
Seven twelves are	→	
Eight twelves are	→	
Nine twelves are	→	
Ten twelves are	→	
Eleven twelves are	→	
Twelve twelves are	→	

Time taken   Seconds

Try the twelve times table in numbers again. Can you beat your last score? Now use the facts from the twelve times table to answer the division questions below.

144 ÷ 12 =
60 ÷ 12 =
120 ÷ 12 =
108 ÷ 12 =
12 ÷ 12 =
96 ÷ 12 =
132 ÷ 12 =
84 ÷ 12 =
36 ÷ 12 =
72 ÷ 12 =
48 ÷ 12 =
24 ÷ 12 =

Time taken   Seconds

Calendar

January	February	March	April
S M T W T F S	S M T W T F S	S M T W T F S	S M T W T F S

May	June	July	August
S M T W T F S	S M T W T F S	S M T W T F S	S M T W T F S

September	October	November	December
S M T W T F S	S M T W T F S	S M T W T F S	S M T W T F S

Brodie's Brain Booster

How many months have you been alive?

More elevens

You should be really fast with the elevens.

An eleven sided shape is sometimes called a hendecagon. Each hendecagon contains a multiple of eleven. Write the multiplication for that multiple. One has been done for you.

88 *8 x 11*

121

33

77

22

99

44

110

11

55

132

66

Brodie's Brain Booster

A farmer groups his sheep in sets of 11. If there are 143 sheep, how many sets are there?

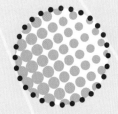

More twelves

Each dodecagon contains a multiple of twelve. Write the multiplication for that multiple. One has been done for you.

48   4 x 12

96

144

24

60

108

132

12

72

36

120

84

Brodie's Brain Booster

How many months are there in twenty years?

Multiple vans!

Use your elevens and twelves.

Each van contains a multiple of eleven or twelve or both. Write the multiplication or multiplications for that multiple. One has been done for you.

72   6 x 12

144

77

22

48

99

24

121

60

132

96

36

88

120

110

66

33

84

1 Write the multiples of 11 from 11 to 132.

2 What is the next multiple of 11 after 132?

3 Write the multiples of 12 from 12 to 144.

4 What is the next multiple of 12 after 144?

5 Count down in twelves. Write the next numbers in this sequence:
144 132 120 108

6 Write the twelve times table as quickly as you can.

$1 \times 12 =$

Now answer these questions.

7 $144 \div 12 =$ **8** $121 \div 11 =$ **9** $96 \div 12 =$

10 $72 \div 12 =$ **11** $132 \div 11 =$ **12** $84 \div 12 =$

Which table is your fastest?

How quickly can you complete each table? Time yourself.

1 x 2 =	1 x 3 =	1 x 4 =	1 x 5 =
2 x 2 =	2 x 3 =	2 x 4 =	2 x 5 =
3 x 2 =	3 x 3 =	3 x 4 =	3 x 5 =
4 x 2 =	4 x 3 =	4 x 4 =	4 x 5 =
5 x 2 =	5 x 3 =	5 x 4 =	5 x 5 =
6 x 2 =	6 x 3 =	6 x 4 =	6 x 5 =
7 x 2 =	7 x 3 =	7 x 4 =	7 x 5 =
8 x 2 =	8 x 3 =	8 x 4 =	8 x 5 =
9 x 2 =	9 x 3 =	9 x 4 =	9 x 5 =
10 x 2 =	10 x 3 =	10 x 4 =	10 x 5 =
11 x 2 =	11 x 3 =	11 x 4 =	11 x 5 =
12 x 2 =	12 x 3 =	12 x 4 =	12 x 5 =

Time taken — Seconds

How quickly can you answer these ten division questions?

40 ÷ 5 =	36 ÷ 4 =	15 ÷ 3 =	30 ÷ 5 =
24 ÷ 2 =	35 ÷ 5 =	18 ÷ 3 =	32 ÷ 4 =
25 ÷ 5 =	24 ÷ 3 =		

Time taken — Seconds

Tables speed

Which table is your fastest?

How quickly can you complete each table? Time yourself.

1 x 6 =	1 x 7 =	1 x 8 =	1 x 9 =
2 x 6 =	2 x 7 =	2 x 8 =	2 x 9 =
3 x 6 =	3 x 7 =	3 x 8 =	3 x 9 =
4 x 6 =	4 x 7 =	4 x 8 =	4 x 9 =
5 x 6 =	5 x 7 =	5 x 8 =	5 x 9 =
6 x 6 =	6 x 7 =	6 x 8 =	6 x 9 =
7 x 6 =	7 x 7 =	7 x 8 =	7 x 9 =
8 x 6 =	8 x 7 =	8 x 8 =	8 x 9 =
9 x 6 =	9 x 7 =	9 x 8 =	9 x 9 =
10 x 6 =	10 x 7 =	10 x 8 =	10 x 9 =
11 x 6 =	11 x 7 =	11 x 8 =	11 x 9 =
12 x 6 =	12 x 7 =	12 x 8 =	12 x 9 =

Time taken — Seconds

How quickly can you answer these ten division questions?

49 ÷ 7 =	36 ÷ 9 =	72 ÷ 8 =	32 ÷ 8 =
48 ÷ 6 =	35 ÷ 7 =	64 ÷ 8 =	72 ÷ 9 =
40 ÷ 8 =	72 ÷ 6 =		

Time taken — Seconds

34

Tables speed

The twenty-fives are very useful.

How quickly can you complete each table? Time yourself.

1 x 10 =	1 x 11 =	1 x 12 =	1 x 25 = 25
2 x 10 =	2 x 11 =	2 x 12 =	2 x 25 = 50
3 x 10 =	3 x 11 =	3 x 12 =	3 x 25 = 75
4 x 10 =	4 x 11 =	4 x 12 =	4 x 25 = 100
5 x 10 =	5 x 11 =	5 x 12 =	5 x 25 = 125
6 x 10 =	6 x 11 =	6 x 12 =	6 x 25 =
7 x 10 =	7 x 11 =	7 x 12 =	7 x 25 =
8 x 10 =	8 x 11 =	8 x 12 =	8 x 25 =
9 x 10 =	9 x 11 =	9 x 12 =	9 x 25 =
10 x 10 =	10 x 11 =	10 x 12 =	10 x 25 =
11 x 10 =	11 x 11 =	11 x 12 =	11 x 25 =
12 x 10 =	12 x 11 =	12 x 12 =	12 x 25 =

Time taken — Seconds

How quickly can you answer these ten division questions?

121 ÷ 11 =	36 ÷ 12 =	100 ÷ 25 =
100 ÷ 4 =	48 ÷ 12 =	96 ÷ 12 =
132 ÷ 11 =	72 ÷ 12 =	
175 ÷ 25 =	110 ÷ 10 =	

Time taken — Seconds

Multiplication square

A multiplication square shows all the tables.

Each answer on the multiplication square is made from multiplying a top number by a side number.

This multiplication square has some of the tables facts missing. Can you fill in the missing facts?

x	1	2	3	4	5	6	7	8	9	10	11	12
1												
2												
3												
4												48
5											55	
6								48				
7												
8						48						
9												
10												
11					55						121	
12				48								

Mixed up multiplication square

The numbers are mixed up on this square.

Each answer on the multiplication square is made from multiplying a top number by a side number.

This multiplication square has some of the tables facts missing. Can you fill in the missing facts?

x	4	9	12	7	2	11	5	10	3	6	8
3											
8		72									
2											
10											
7						77					
9										54	72
5											
12						132				72	
4											
11			132	77							
6		54	72								

37

1 Write the multiples of 2 from 2 to 24.

2 Write the multiples of 3 from 3 to 36.

3 Write the multiples of 4 from 4 to 48.

4 Write the multiples of 5 from 5 to 60.

5 Write the multiples of 6 from 6 to 72.

6 Write the multiples of 7 from 7 to 84.

7 Write the multiples of 8 from 8 to 96.

8 Write the multiples of 9 from 9 to 108.

9 Write the multiples of 10 from 10 to 120.

10 Write the multiples of 11 from 11 to 132.

11 Write the multiples of 12 from 12 to 144.

Now answer these questions.

12 $36 \div 9 =$

13 $200 \div 25 =$

14 $48 \div 6 =$

15 $121 \div 11 =$

16 $132 \div 12 =$

17 $54 \div 9 =$

18 $150 \div 25 =$

19 $72 \div 8 =$

20 $81 \div 9 =$

Factors

Look at the multiplications that make 12.

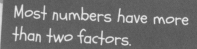
Most numbers have more than two factors.

1 X 12   2 X 6

4 X 3   **12**   3 X 4

6 X 2   12 X 1

The numbers 1, 2, 3, 4, 6 and 12 are the factors of 12.

Write the multiplications that make 20.

20

Brodie's Brain Booster
How many factors does the number 10 have?

Write the multiplications that make 18.

18

More factors

Write the multiplications that make 16.

16

Write the multiplications that make 22.

22

Write the factors for each number below.

2

3

4

5

6

7

8

9

10

11

12

Brodie's Brain Booster

How many factors does the number 48 have?

Square numbers

The smallest square number is 1.

Look carefully at the dot patterns.

1 x 1   2 x 2   3 x 3   4 x 4

Write the answers to the questions below. They are all called square numbers.

1 x 1 =   2 x 2 =   3 x 3 =   4 x 4 =

5 x 5 =   6 x 6 =   7 x 7 =   8 x 8 =

9 x 9 =   10 x 10 =   11 x 11 =   12 x 12 =

Instead of writing 1 x 1 we can write 1^2 so $1^2 = 1$ and $2^2 = 4$.

Write the answers to the questions below. All the answers are already shown above.

$7^2 =$ $5^2 =$ $8^2 =$ $10^2 =$

$3^2 =$ $6^2 =$ $11^2 =$ $4^2 =$

Brodie's Brain Booster

What's 20 squared?

41

Using the tables

Times tables can help you when multiplying bigger numbers.

Look at this multiplication. We are multiplying 23 by 4.

$$\begin{array}{r} 23 \\ \times\, 4 \\ \hline 9\,2 \\ \end{array}$$

Step 1
3 x 4 = 12

Step 2
2 tens x 4 = 8 tens plus 1 ten to make 9 tens

Now try these.

4 2	2 9	7 6	9 3	5 3
x 3	x 4	x 7	x 8	x 5

8 2	7 8	3 8	4 7	4 1
x 4	x 6	x 9	x 3	x 2

Brodie's Brain Booster
How many days are there altogether in 52 weeks?
How many days are there in one year?

Mini squares

How fast are you?

How quickly can you complete each mini tables square? Time yourself.

x	4	8	3	7	2
2					
9					
6					
5					
7					

x	9	6	1	5	7
8					
3					
9					
4					
2					

Time taken

Seconds

Time taken

Seconds

x	8	3	1	9	4
7					
5					
2					
6					
8					

x	4	9	5	7	3
6					
2					
8					
7					
4					

Time taken

Seconds

Time taken

Seconds

43

1 Write the multiplications that make the number 24.

24

2 What are the factors of 24?

3 Write the multiplications that make the number 32.

32

4 What are the factors of 32?

5 Write the multiplications that make the number 28.

28

6 What are the factors of 28?

Now answer these questions.

7 $6 \times 6 =$

8 $10 \times 10 =$

9 $8^2 =$

10 $144 \div 12 =$

11 $7^2 =$

12 $121 \div 11 =$

13 $81 \div 9 =$

14 $5^2 =$

15 $20^2 =$

ANSWERS

Page 3

2×2=4	6÷2=3
3×2=6	24÷2=12
4×2=8	14÷2=7
5×2=10	12÷2=6
6×2=12	2÷2=1
7×2=14	10÷2=5
8×2=16	22÷2=11
9×2=18	16÷2=8
10×2=20	8÷2=4
11×2=22	20÷2=10
12×2=24	18÷2=9
	4÷2=2

Brain Booster: 25 2p coins

Page 4

1×3=3	9÷3=3
2×3=6	18÷3=6
3×3=9	30÷3=10
4×3=12	27÷3=9
5×3=15	6÷3=2
6×3=18	24÷3=8
7×3=21	21÷3=7
8×3=24	36÷3=12
9×3=27	33÷3=11
10×3=30	15÷3=5
11×3=33	12÷3=4
12×3=36	3÷3=1

Brain Booster: 45 sides

Page 5

9: 3×3
14: 7×2
21: 7×3
15: 5×3
24: 12×2,8×3
4: 2×2
12: 6×2,4×3
27: 9×3
36: 18×2,12×3
16: 8×2
2: 1×2
6: 3×2,2×3
30: 15×2,10×3
8: 4×2
33: 11×3
10: 5×2
20: 10×2

Page 6

1×4=4	4×4=16
2×4=8	5×4=20
3×4=12	6×4=24

7×4=28	32÷4=8
8×4=32	28÷4=7
9×4=36	24÷4=6
10×4=40	40÷4=10
11×4=44	16÷4=4
12×4=48	44÷4=11
8÷4=2	36÷4=9
48÷4=12	12÷4=3
20÷4=5	4÷4=1

Brain Booster: 60 sides

Page 7

7×4=28, 24÷2=12, 12x3=36, 9x4=36
27÷3=9, 2×2=4, 4×4=16, 15÷3=5
12×2=24, 11×4=44, 21÷3=7, 6×2=12
16÷4=4, 3×3=9, 9×2=18, 36÷4=9
7×2=14, 24÷3=8, 48÷4=12, 4×2=8
18÷3=6, 5×4=20, 11×2=22, 6÷3=2
28÷4=7, 8×2=16, 12÷3=4, 12÷4=3
6×3=18, 8÷2=4, 36÷3=12, 8×3=24

60 wheels
60 wheels
25 bikes

Page 8 • Progress Test 1

1. 2, 4, 6, 8, 10, 12
   14, 16, 18, 20, 22, 24
2. 3, 6, 9, 12, 15, 18
   21, 24, 27, 30, 33, 36
3. 4, 8, 12, 16, 20, 24
   28, 32, 36, 40, 44, 48
4. 52
5. 21:7×3
   32:16×2, 8×4
   12:6×2, 4×3, 3×4
   18:9×2, 6×3
   27:9×3
6. 16÷4=4
7. 24÷3=8
8. 22÷2=11
9. 30÷3=10
10. 28÷4=7
11. 36÷4=9
12. 18÷3=6
13. 21÷3=7
14. 18÷2=9

Page 9

1×5=5	7×5=35
2×5=5	8×5=40
3×5=15	9×5=45
4×5=20	10×5=50
5×5=25	11×5=55
6×5=30	12×5=60

35÷5=7	40÷5=8
20÷5=4	25÷5=5
55÷5=11	50÷5=10
5÷5=1	60÷5=12
45÷5=9	15÷5=3
10÷5=2	30÷5=6

Brain Booster: 20 5p coins

Page 10

1×6=6	48÷6=8
2×6=12	12÷6=2
3×6=18	30÷6=5
4×6=24	42÷6=7
5×6=30	66÷6=11
6×6=36	72÷6=12
7×6=42	36÷6=6
8×6=48	24÷6=4
9×6=54	6÷6=1
10×6=60	18÷6=3
11×6=66	60÷6=10
12×6=72	54÷6=9

Brain Booster: 90 eggs

Page 11

18: 3×6
30: 5×6
42: 7×6
66: 11×6
6: 1×6
24: 4×6
60: 10×6
72: 12×6
36: 6×6
12: 2×6
54: 9×6

Brain Booster:16 boxes

Page 12

Check that your child has drawn lines to match the questions to the answers

2×6=12	9×6=54
7×5=35	6×5=30
12×5=60	12×6=72
8×6=48	11×6=66
2×5=10	4×5=20
9×5=45	5×6=30
10×6=60	6×6=36
8×5=40	7×6=42
4×6=24	5×5=25

Brain Booster: 90

Page 13

24: 4×6
42: 7×6
66: 11×6
25: 5×5
72: 12×6
15: 3×5
60: 12×5, 10×6
45: 9×5
12: 2×6
36: 6×6
10: 2×5
35: 7×5
18: 3×6
20: 4×5
48: 8×6
40: 8×5
54: 9×6

Page 14 • Progress Test 2

1. 6, 12, 18, 24, 30, 36
   42, 48, 54, 60, 66, 72
2. 5, 10, 15, 20, 25, 30, 35, 40, 45, 50
   55, 60, 65, 70, 75, 80, 85, 90, 95, 100
3. 108 eggs
4. 14 5p coins
5. £2
6. 36÷6=6
7. 45÷5=9
8. 24÷6=4
9. 30÷5=6
10. 72÷6=12
11. 55÷5=11
12. 42÷6=7
13. 35÷5=7
14. 48÷6=8

Page 15

1×7=7	42÷7=6
2×7=14	14÷7=2
3×7=21	49÷7=7
4×7=28	84÷7=12
5×7=35	77÷7=11
6×7=42	35÷7=5
7×7=49	7÷7=1
8×7=56	63÷7=9
9×7=63	56÷7=8
10×7=70	28÷7=4
11×7=77	70÷7=10
12×7=84	21÷7=3

Brain Booster: 98 days

Page 16

1×8=8	32÷8=4
2×8=16	64÷8=8
3×8=24	80÷8=10
4×8=32	16÷8=2
5×8=40	72÷8=9
6×8=48	56÷8=7
7×8=56	48÷8=6
8×8=64	8÷8=1
9×8=72	40÷8=5
10×8=80	88÷8=11
11×8=88	24÷8=3
12×8=96	96÷8=12

Brain Booster: 120 legs

Page 17

49: 7×7	21: 3×7	42: 6×7
84: 12×7	56: 8×7	63: 9×7
77: 11×7	7: 1×7	14: 2×7
28: 4×7	70: 10×7	35: 5×7

Brain Booster: 98 sides

Page 18

56: 7×8	96: 12×8	16: 2×8
64: 8×8	32: 4×8	48: 6×8
8: 1×8	72: 12×8	88: 11×8
24: 6×8	40: 5×8	80: 10×8

Brain Booster: 136 arms

Page 19

48: 6×8	24: 3×8	42: 6×7
64: 8×8	56: 8×7,7×8	70: 10×7
16: 2×8	72: 9×8	96: 12×8
28: 4×7	49: 7×7	40: 5×8
80: 10×8	32: 4×8	14: 2×7
35: 5x7	21: 3×7	88: 11×8

Page 20 • Progress Test 3

1. 7, 14, 21, 28, 35, 42
   49, 56, 63, 70, 77, 84
2. 91
3. 8, 16, 24, 32, 40, 48
   56, 64, 72, 80, 88, 96
4. 104
5. 32:4×8
   42:6×7
   56:8×7,7×8
   84:12×7
   96:12×8
6. 42÷7=6
7. 48÷8=6
8. 28÷7=4
9. 72÷8=9
10. 56÷7=8
11. 64÷8=8
12. 96÷8=12

Page 21

1×9=9	36÷9=4
2×9=18	99÷9=11
3×9=27	81÷9=9
4×9=36	108÷9=12
5×9=45	72÷9=8
6×9=54	63÷9=7
7×9=63	45÷9=5
8×9=72	27÷9=3
9×9=81	90÷9=10
10×9=90	18÷9=2
11×9=99	9÷9=1
12×9=108	54÷9=6

Brain Booster: 360

Page 22

1×10=10	100÷10=10
2×10=20	90÷10=9
3×10=30	40÷10=4
4×10=40	10÷10=1
5×10=50	60÷10=6
6×10=60	70÷10=7
7×10=70	110÷10=11
8×10=80	50÷10=5
9×10=90	30÷10=3
10×10=100	120÷10=12
11×10=110	20÷10=2
12×10=120	80÷10=8

Brain Booster: 1000

Page 23

63: 7×9	99: 11×9	27: 3×9
54: 6×9	18: 2×9	36: 4×9
108: 12×9	72: 8×9	9: 1×9
81: 9×9	45: 5×9	90: 10×9

Brain Booster: 144

Page 24

43×10=430	179×10=1790
18×10=180	
864×10=8640	99×10=990
277×10=2770	
4.5×10=45	27.6×10=276
4.99×10=49.9	
0.7×10=7	0.37×10=3.7
48.64×10=486.4	

Brain Booster: £5.80

Page 25

81: 9×9	40: 4×10	
27: 3×9	108: 12×9	120: 12×10
72: 8×9	60: 6×10	36: 6×6
80: 8×10	18: 2×9	110: 11×10
63: 7×9	45: 5×9	70: 7×10
99: 11×9	30: 3×10	54: 6×9

Page 26 • Progress Test 4

1. 10, 20, 30, 40, 50, 60, 70, 80, 90, 100
   110, 120, 130, 140, 150, 160, 170,
   180, 190, 200
2. 9, 18, 27, 36, 45, 54
   63, 72, 81, 90, 99, 108
3. 117
4. 20 corners
5. 108 corners
6. 1×9=9, 2×9=18, 3×9=27, 4×9=36
   5×9=45, 6×9=54, 7×9=63, 8×9=72
   9×9=81, 10×9=90, 11×9=99,
   12×9=108
7. 54÷9=6
8. 36÷9=4
9. 81÷9=9
10. 108÷9=12
11. 12.4×10=124
12. 6.35×10=63.5

Page 27

1×11=11	121÷11=11
2×11=22	33÷11=3
3×11=33	66÷11=6
4×11=44	11÷11=1
5×11=55	110÷11=10
6×11=66	99÷11=9
7×11=77	55÷11=5
8×11=88	22÷11=2
9×11=99	88÷11=8
10×11=110	132÷11=12
11×11=121	77÷11=7
12×11=132	44÷11=4

Brain Booster: 165

Page 28

1×12=12	144÷12=12
2×12=24	60÷12=5
3×12=36	120÷12=10
4×12=48	108÷12=9
5×12=60	12÷12=1
6×12=72	96÷12=8
7×12=84	132÷12=11
8×12=96	84÷12=7
9×12=108	36÷12=3
10×12=120	72÷12=6
11×12=132	48÷12=4
12×12=144	24÷12=2

Brain Booster: Check that your child has calculated the correct number of months

Page 29

88: 8×11	121: 11×11	33: 3×11
77: 7×11	22: 2×11	99: 9×11
44: 4×11	110: 10×11	11: 1×11
55: 5×11	132: 12×11	66: 6×11

Brain Booster: 13 sets

Page 30

48: 4×12	96: 8×12	144: 12×12
24: 2×12	60: 5×12	108: 9×12
132: 11×12	12: 1×12	72: 6×12
36: 3×12	120: 10×12	84: 7×12

Brain Booster: 240 months

Page 31

144: 12×12	77: 7×11	
22: 2×11	48: 4×12	99: 9×11
24: 2×12	121: 11×11	60: 5×12
132: 12×11,11×12	96: 8×12	36: 3×12
88: 8×11	120: 10×12	110: 10×11
66: 6×11	33: 3×11	84: 7×12

Page 32 • Progress Test 5

1. 11, 22, 33, 44, 55, 66
   77, 88, 99, 110, 121, 132
2. 143
3. 12, 24, 36, 48, 60, 72
   84, 96, 108, 120, 132, 144
4. 156
5. 96, 84, 72, 60, 48, 36, 24, 12
6. 1×12=12, 2×12=24, 3×12=36,
   4×12=48
   5×12=60, 6×12=72, 7×12=84,
   8×12=96
   9×12=108, 10×12=120, 11×12=132,
   12×12=144
7. 144÷12=12
8. 121÷11=11
9. 96÷12=8
10. 72÷12=6
11. 132÷11=12
12. 84÷12=7

Page 33

1×2=2	1×3=3
2×2=4	2×3=6
3×2=6	3×3=9
4×2=8	4×3=12
5×2=10	5×3=15
6×2=12	6×3=18
7×2=14	7×3=21
8×2=16	8×3=24
9×2=18	9×3=27
10×2=20	10×3=30
11×2=22	11×3=33
12×2=24	12×3=36

1×4=4	1×5=5
2×4=8	2×5=10
3×4=12	3×5=15
4×4=16	4×5=20
5×4=20	5×5=25
6×4=24	6×5=30
7×4=28	7×5=35
8×4=32	8×5=40
9×4=36	9×5=45
10×4=40	10×5=50
11×4=44	11×5=55
12×4=48	12×5=60

40÷5=8, 36÷4=9, 15÷3=5, 30÷5=6
24÷2=12, 35÷5=7, 18÷3=6, 32÷4=8
25÷5=5, 24÷3=8

Page 34

1×6=6	1×7=7
2×6=12	2×7=14
3×6=18	3×7=21
4×6=24	4×7=28
5×6=30	5×7=35
6×6=36	6×7=42
7×6=42	7×7=49
8×6=48	8×7=56
9×6=54	9×7=63
10×6=60	10×7=70
11×6=66	11×7=77
12×6=72	12×7=84

1×8=8	1×9=9
2×8=16	2×9=18
3×8=24	3×9=27
4×8=32	4×9=36
5×8=40	5×9=45
6×8=48	6×9=54
7×8=56	7×9=63
8×8=64	8×9=72
9×8=72	9×9=81
10×8=80	10×9=90
11×8=88	11×9=99
12×8=96	12×9=108

49÷7=7, 36÷9=4, 72÷9=8, 32÷8=4
48÷6=8, 35÷7=5, 64÷8=8, 72÷9=8
40÷8=5, 72÷6=12

Page 35

1×10=10	1×11=11
2×10=20	2×11=22
3×10=30	3×11=33
4×10=40	4×11=44
5×10=50	5×11=55
6×10=60	6×11=66
7×10=70	7×11=77
8×10=80	8×11=88
9×10=90	9×11=99
10×10=100	10×11=110

11×10=110   11×11=121
12×10=120   12×11=132

1×12=12   1×25=25
2×12=24   2×25=50
3×12=36   3×25=75
4×12=48   4×25=100
5×12=60   5×15=125
6×12=72   6×25=150
7×12=84   7×25=175
8×12=96   8×25=200
9×12=108   9×25=225
10×12=120   10×25=250
11×12=132   11×25=275
12×12=144   12×25=300

121÷11=11, 36÷12=3, 100÷25=4
100÷4=25, 48÷12=4, 96÷12=8
132÷11=12, 72÷12=6
175÷25=7, 110÷10=11

Page 36

1, 2, 3, 4, 5, 6, 7, 8, 9, 10, 11, 12
2, 4, 6, 8, 10, 12, 14, 16, 18, 20, 22, 24
3, 6, 9, 12, 15, 18, 21, 24, 27, 30, 33, 36
4, 8, 12, 16, 20, 24, 28, 32, 36, 40, 44, 48
5, 10, 15, 20, 25, 30, 35, 40, 45, 50, 55, 60
6, 12, 18, 24, 30, 36, 42, 48, 54, 60, 66, 72
7, 14, 21, 28, 35, 42, 49, 56, 63, 70, 77, 84
8, 16, 24, 32, 40, 48, 56, 64, 72, 80, 88, 96
9, 18, 27, 36, 45, 54, 63, 72, 81, 90, 99, 108
10, 20, 30, 40, 50, 60, 70, 80, 90, 100, 110, 120
11, 22, 33, 44, 55, 66, 77, 88, 99, 110, 121, 132
12, 24, 36, 48, 60, 72, 84, 96, 108, 120, 132, 144

Page 37

12, 27, 36, 21, 6, 33, 15, 30, 9, 18, 24
32, 72, 96, 56, 16, 88, 40, 80, 24, 48, 64
8, 18, 24, 14, 4, 22, 10, 20, 6, 12, 16
40, 90, 120, 70, 20, 110, 50, 100, 30, 60, 80
28, 63, 84, 49, 14, 77, 35, 70, 21, 42, 56
36, 81, 108, 63, 18, 99, 45, 90, 27, 54, 72
20, 45, 60, 35, 10, 55, 25, 50, 15, 30, 40
48, 108, 144, 84, 24, 132, 60, 120, 36, 72, 96
16, 36, 48, 28, 8, 44, 20, 40, 12, 24, 32
44, 99, 132, 77, 22, 121, 55, 110, 33, 66, 88
24, 54, 72, 42, 12, 66, 30, 60, 18, 36, 48

Page 38 • Progress Test 6

1. 2, 4, 6, 8, 10, 12, 14, 16, 18, 20, 22, 24
2. 3, 6, 9, 12, 15, 18, 21, 24, 27, 30, 33, 36
3. 4, 8, 12, 16, 20, 24, 28, 32, 36, 40, 44, 48
4. 5, 10, 15, 20, 25, 30, 35, 40, 45, 50, 55, 60
5. 6, 12, 18, 24, 30, 36, 42, 48, 54, 60, 66, 72
6. 7, 14, 21, 28, 35, 42, 49, 56, 63, 70, 77, 84

7. 8, 16, 24, 32, 40, 48, 56, 64, 72, 80, 88, 96
8. 9, 18, 27, 36, 45, 54, 63, 72, 81, 90, 99, 108
9. 10, 20, 30, 40, 50, 60, 70, 80, 90, 100, 110, 120
10. 11, 22, 33, 44, 55, 66, 77, 88, 99, 110, 121, 132
11. 12, 24, 36, 48, 60, 72, 84, 96, 108, 120, 132, 144
12. 36÷9=4
13. 200÷25=8
14. 48÷6=8
15. 121÷11=11
16. 132÷12=11
17. 54÷9=6
18. 150÷25=6
19. 72÷8=9
20. 81÷9=9

Page 39

20: 1×20, 2×10, 4×5, 5×4, 10×2, 20×1
18: 1×18, 2×9, 3×6, 6×3, 9×2, 18×1

Brain Booster: 4 factors (1, 2, 5, 10)

Page 40

16: 1×16, 2×8, 4×4, 8×2, 16×1
22: 1×22, 2×11, 11×2, 22×1

2: 1, 2
3: 1, 3
4: 1, 2, 4
5: 1, 5
6: 1, 2, 3, 6
7: 1, 7
8: 1, 2, 4, 8
9: 1, 3, 9
10: 1, 2, 5, 10
11: 1, 11
12: 1, 2, 3, 4, 6, 12

Brain Booster: 10 factors (1, 2, 3, 4, 6, 8, 12, 16, 24, 48)

Page 41

1×1=1, 2×2=4, 3×3=9, 4×4=16
5×5=25, 6×6=36, 7×7=49, 8×8=64
9×9=81, 10×10=100, 11×11=121, 12×12=144

7^2=49, 5^2=25, 8^2=64, 10^2=100
3^2=9, 6^2=36, 11^2=121, 4^2 =16

Brain Booster: 400

Page 42

42×3=126, 29×4=116, 76×7=532, 93×8=744, 53×5=265
82×4=328, 78×6=468, 38×9=342, 47×3=141, 41×2=82

Brain Booster: 364 days in 52 weeks. 365 days in one year.

Page 43

8, 16, 6, 14, 4
36, 72, 27, 63, 18
24, 48, 18, 42, 12
20, 40, 15, 35, 10
28, 56, 21, 49, 14

72, 48, 8, 40, 56
27, 18, 3, 15, 21
81, 54, 9, 45, 63
36, 24, 4, 20, 28
18, 12, 2, 10, 14

56, 21, 7, 63, 28
40, 15, 5, 45, 20
16, 6, 2, 18, 8
48, 18, 6, 54, 24
64, 24, 8, 72, 32

24, 54, 30, 42, 18
8, 18, 10, 14, 6
32, 72, 40, 56, 24
28, 63, 35, 49, 21
16, 36, 20, 28, 12

Page 44 • Progress Test 7

1. 1×24, 2×12, 3×8, 4×6, 6×4, 8×3, 12×2, 24×1
2. 1, 2, 3, 4, 6, 8, 12, 24
3. 1×32, 2×16, 4×8, 8×4, 16×2, 32×1
4. 1, 2, 4, 8, 16, 32
5. 1×28, 2×14, 4×7, 7×4, 14×2, 28×1
6. 1, 2, 4, 7, 14, 28
7. 6×6=36
8. 10×10=100
9. 8^2=64
10. 144÷12=12
11. 7^2=49
12. 121÷11=11
13. 81÷9=9
14. 5^2=25
15. 20^2=400